WALKS ALONG THE WEST
JURASSIC COAST

PORTLAND TO EXMOUTH

Robert Westwood

JURASSIC
COAST
TRUST

A Jurassic Coast Trust Book

Author Robert Westwood
Editor Alison Moss
Design Jonathan Lewis
Production Peter Sills

First published as *Walking the West Jurassic Coast Orcombe Point to the Fleet* in 2010,
this revised edition printed in 2018
Jurassic Coast Trust
Mountfield, Rax Lane, Bridport
Dorset DT6 3JP
Tel: 01308 807000
Email: info@jurassiccoast.org
www.jurassiccoast.org

ISBN 978-1-907701-14-6

British Library Cataloguing-in-Publication Data
A catalogue record for this book is available from the British Library.

Any views or opinions expressed in this publication are solely those of the
authors and do not necessarily represent those of the publisher.

In the interests of your personal safety and enjoyment of the World Heritage Site,
the Jurassic Coast Trust recommend that you follow fully all the relevant
safety advice in this book and the Fossil and The Countryside Codes.
The Jurassic Coast Trust can accept no liability whatsoever.

Your purchase supports our work to protect the Jurassic Coast and help anybody and everybody to love,
understand and value it. (Jurassic Coast Trust Registered charity: 1101134) www.jurassiccoast.org

This publication was first published by Coastal Publishing Limited and the Jurassic Coast Trust is grateful
to Peter Sills and Coastal Publishing for their contribution to the World Heritage Site. This edition has
been reprinted by the Jurassic Coast Trust.

Front cover image: East Cliff, West Bay.

Printed and bound in the United Kingdom.

For guided walks along the Jurassic Coast with the author Robert Westwood see
www.jurassiccoastwalking.co.uk

Image Acknowledgements
(Key: t:top, m:middle, b:bottom, l:left, r:right)
Images in this book are copyright of the photographers and artists.

Front cover © Coastal Publishing Ltd
All aerial photography and 4-5t, 17 © Coastal Publishing Ltd
Other photography © Robert Westwood except Steve Trewhella: 8m; Bryan
Edwards: 9t; Martin Cade: 9b; Richard Edmonds: 24b; Lyme Regis Museum:
35t; Dorset County Council: 39r; Richard Edwards: 44b; June Woodger: 51m;
Devon County Council: 63t.

Cross sections © 2000/2013: Dorset County Council, M.R. House, R.A. Edwards
and The Jurassic Coast Trust with most of the Dorset sections based on the
work of House (1993).The sections from Lyme Regis to Exmouth are based on
that in Edwards (2008).

The Jurassic Coast Trust and the author have made every reasonable effort to locate, contact and
acknowledge copyright owners and wishes to be informed by any copyright owners who are not
properly identified and acknowledged so that we may make any necessary corrections.

CONTENTS

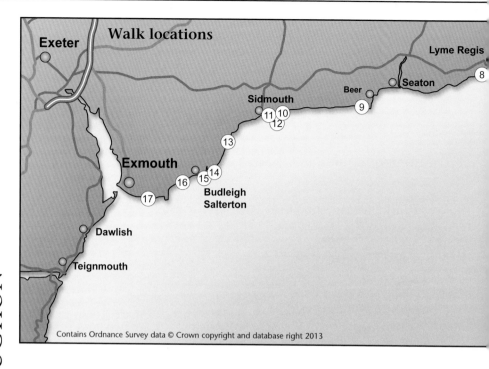

Walk locations

Exeter
Lyme Regis
Seaton (8)
Beer (9)
Sidmouth (11)(10)
(12)
(13)
Exmouth (14)
(16)(15)
Budleigh
Salterton (17)
Dawlish
Teignmouth

Contains Ordnance Survey data © Crown copyright and database right 2013

The Jurassic Coast World Heritage Site begins at Orcombe Point near Exmouth, Devon, and ends at Handfast Point near Swanage, Dorset. This walking guide covers the western part of the coast from The Fleet to Exmouth. There are stunning walks to interest everyone; most can be completed by all the family in a few hours, while some are short strolls. Many of the walks are circular; walks 3, 4, 6, 10 and 12 are one way but the excellent local transport can be used to arrive back at the start point.

We start with a feature that is only a few thousand years old, virtually yesterday in geological terms. The 18-mile long Chesil Beach stretches from the Isle of Portland to West Bay and provides some unique and wonderful scenery for the first two walks of the guide.

The beginning of the Jurassic Period saw shallow tropical seas over what is now the Devon and Dorset coast. Many different sorts of sediments were formed with an astounding range of fossils preserved in them, making Lyme Bay one of the world's most important fossil locations. The area then returned to land and many Jurassic sediments were eroded away before Cretaceous seas once more laid down new sediments. We finish with the spectacular Triassic red cliffs of east Devon, deposited in arid deserts when the landmass of the Earth formed one huge continent, known as Pangaea. The walks have been chosen to illustrate the fascinating geology and each one has a particular point of interest, hopefully giving an idea of how this beautiful landscape was formed and perhaps even stimulating further enquiry.

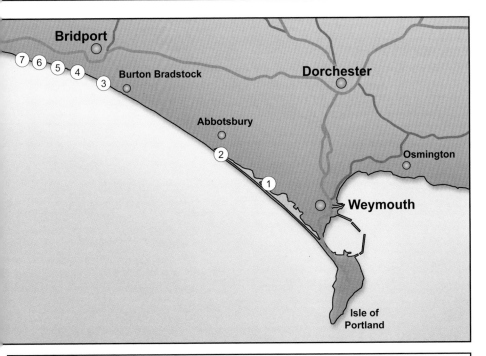

SAFETY FIRST!

Rockfalls and mudslides are an ever-present hazard on this coast and you are most strongly advised to stay away from the base of the cliffs and the cliff top. See page 64 for more information about safety and fossil collecting.

Transport

Public Transport is an excellent way to explore the Jurassic Coast. Poole, Weymouth, Exmouth and Exeter have good rail links to start you on your journey and there are also a range of excellent bus services that serve the towns and villages along the way, including the famous X53, Jurassic Coaster, run by First Bus.

However, bus services change over time and are managed by different operators the length of the coast. We suggest that you check details before starting your journey. Information can be found on the Jurassic Coast Trust website,

www.jurassiccoast.org/travel but we also recommend that you look at www.travelinesw.com or call Travel Line 0871 200 2233.

There are also a number of boat services, either tours or taxi style services at different locations along the coast, why not enquire in your accommodation or TIC as to whether this might add a different dimension to your walk.

Most walks give information about the nearest car park.

Langton
Herring

Start/Finish

P

THE FLEET

Moonfleet
Manor

Chesil Beach

The Fleet

East
Fleet

Walk 1- The Fleet

Distance	7.5 miles (12km)
Estimated time	3 hours
Difficulty	••••
Ascent	300ft (90m)
Map	OS Map OL 15
Starting point	SY 610827

Notes: A long but fairly level walk with one or two moderate climbs.

In Langton Herring follow the road to the end of the village. There is a small layby near the sewage works. Take the path opposite the works, turn left through the gate at the end and on down the path to the Fleet. Then follow the coast path past Moonfleet Manor and East Fleet where you can see the old church that was swamped in the tidal wave of 1824. Moonfleet was, of course, the setting for the book of the same name by J. Meade Falkner.

Follow the little path past the church on to the road heading north-north-west, past the new church. At the top of the road there is an entrance to a campsite; take the straight path to your right heading north. Turn left through the campsite (by the Red Barn) and follow the path back to the Fleet. Turn right following the sign back to Langton Herring.

WALK 1

The Fleet at Rodden Hive.

To the north of Chesil Beach lie the calm waters of the Fleet Lagoon, a shallow stretch of brackish water formed as the beach was pushed landward by rising sea levels. It is open to the sea via a narrow channel at Ferrybridge near Portland, and at this point it is about as saline as sea water, gradually becoming much less saline towards Abbotsbury. Most of the Fleet is no more than 2 metres deep.

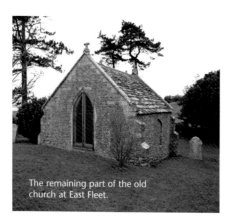

The remaining part of the old church at East Fleet.

As well as the world-famous swannery, the Fleet is home to many rare and endangered species of plants, birds and fish.

It is a Special Area of Conservation and a Site of Special Scientific Interest. Up to 5,000 brent geese over-winter here and it is a designated bass nursery. Much information can be found at www.dorsetwildlifetrust.org.uk/chesilbeach.html including links to sites that record bird sightings.

The water in the Fleet is a mix of fresh water entering via streams and springs and seawater which percolates through Chesil Beach. During storms sea water can flow through much more quickly and often forms 'Canns' or hollows on the landward side of the beach.

Sea Pea growing on the beach near Abbotsbury.

Many shipwrecks have been recorded off Chesil Beach, often caused by storm-force southwesterly winds driving stricken vessels onto the shingle.

Dark-bellied brent geese can be seen on the mudflats at Ferrybridge during the winter.

In 1824 a great storm struck leading to many deaths. A huge wave swept over the beach, destroying the village of Fleet and flooding large areas around Abbotsbury. Although generally regarded as simply a huge storm wave, it has been suggested that this wave may have been a 'meteorological tsunami'; that is, a tidal wave caused not by seismic activity but by weather conditions. It may be that some storm waves are long period waves caused by a number of conditions associated with intense low-pressure areas. At the old church in Fleet it is recorded that the water reached a depth of around 30 feet. The coastline of southern England is not generally regarded as being at risk from tidal waves but it may be that we should be more aware of the potential threat from such freak waves caused by severe weather conditions.

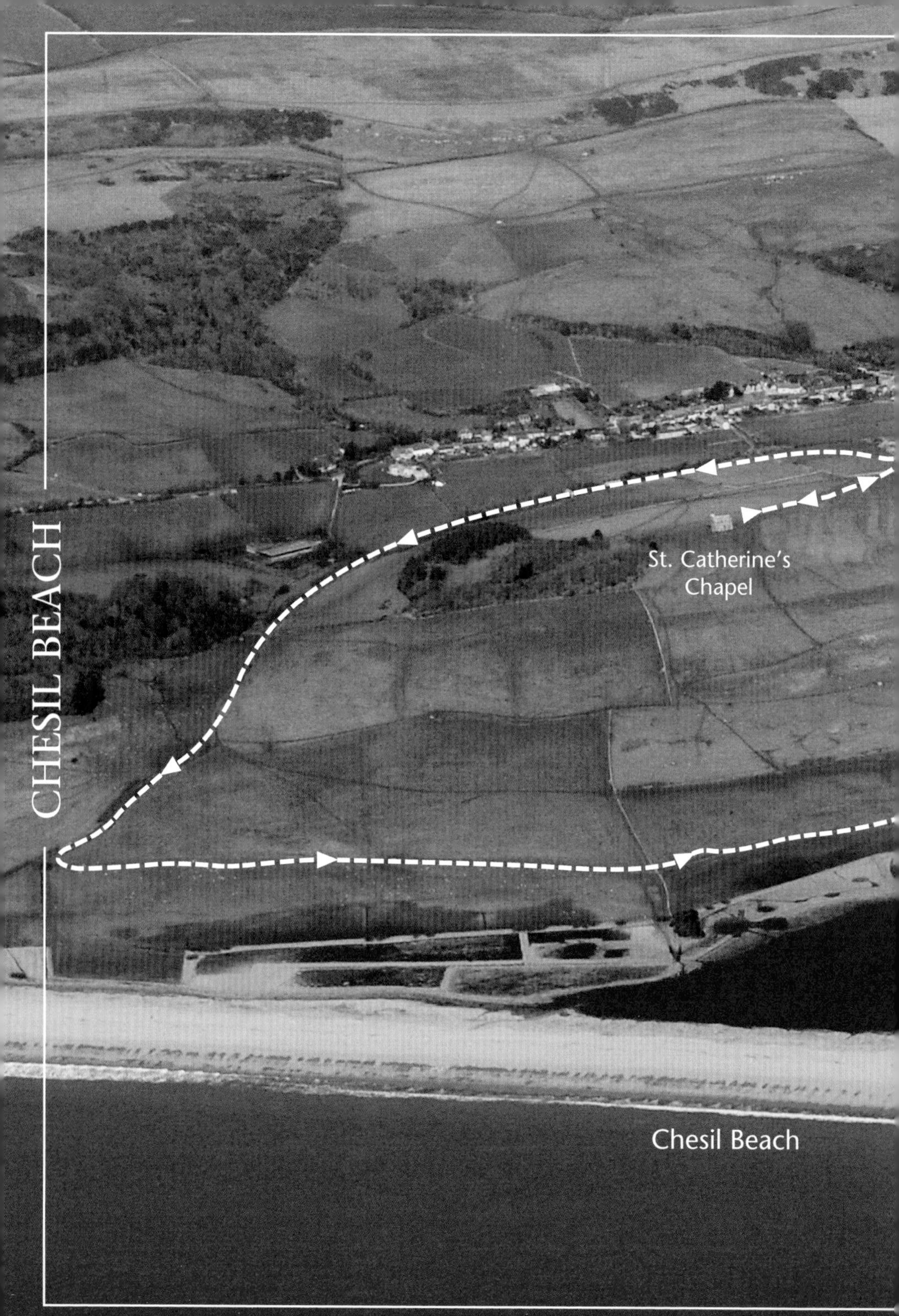

CHESIL BEACH

St. Catherine's
Chapel

Chesil Beach

Abbotsbury

P Start/Finish

Tithe Barn

Abbotsbury Swannery

The Fleet

Walk 2 - The Fleet Shore & Abbotsbury

Distance	3.1 miles (5km)
Estimated time	1½ hours
Difficulty	●●○○○
Ascent	290ft (60m)
Map	OS Map OL 15
Starting point	SY 578853

Notes: A very easy walk, but it is well worth the climb up the hill to St Catherine's Chapel.

This is an easy walk taking in the lovely village of Abbotsbury. It starts at the main car park in the centre of the village, easily found on the left as you enter it from the east on the B3157. From the car park follow the road westwards and around the sharp bend to the right.

As the road straightens out take a path to the left towards St Catherine's Chapel. After a little way the path curves around to the right but it is worth going straight on to climb the hill and see the chapel; the views from the top are amazing.

Return the same way and continue along the path that curves around the hill towards Chesil Beach. Go past the South West Coast Path on the left and then take another path on the left, a permissive path to Abbotsbury Swannery, which goes beside the reed beds. When you reach a stile on your right go over this towards the Swannery and then left up the small road. Continue up the road a little way before taking a path on the left over a stile signed 'Coast Path' and 'Rope

Chesil Beach just west of Abbotsbury.

Walk'. This will join up with the path you took at the start of the walk.

The geological focus throughout most of this book is on processes that went on many millions of years ago; Chesil Beach, by contrast, is a very recent phenomenon, achieving its present state as recently as 4,000–5,000 years ago. It stretches some 18 miles from West Bay to the cliffs of Portland and is a world-famous example of a linear storm beach. As the name suggests, storms were prominent in its formation and it has long been conjectured that storms are a very important agent in geological history. The formation of Chesil Beach continues to be a subject of debate.

During the Ice Age sea levels were about 120m lower than they are today as so much water was locked up in great ice sheets. Although Devon and Dorset were not covered by ice, it was not far away and conditions would have been those of a barren, arctic tundra with freezing and thawing through the seasons. As a result, the cliffs degraded and large amounts of debris accumulated on the dried up sea floor. One theory for the formation of the beach is that as the ice sheets melted about 20,000 years ago, rising seas swept up the weathered material and drove the beach onshore, trapping the Fleet lagoon behind it. But a second theory adds the idea that the rising seas encountered vast, degraded landslides in West Dorset and East Devon and as these eroded, they generated a huge volume of shingle that was carried east by long shore drift, to form the beach. Like many rival theories, the truth is probably a combination of both but the important thing to consider is that the process that formed the beach has essentially stopped and therefore the beach must be in terminal decline and will, at some stage in the future, be breached by the sea.

Abbotsbury and the Swannery

Abbotsbury lies at the western end of the Fleet, the natural lagoon that formed when Chesil Beach moved onshore as sea levels rose. The reeds that grew in this shallow, brackish water provided an ideal nesting place for birds. Early in the eleventh century a Benedictine monastery was founded here on the orders of King Canute; it is not known exactly when, but the monks started farming swans in the lagoon to provide fresh meat. It continued until the dissolution of the monasteries in 1539 when it was purchased by the Strangways family, descendants of whom have owned it ever since. It is the only managed colony of nesting mute swans in the world.

The solid geology of the coast around Abbotsbury is obscured by the Fleet and Chesil Beach, but the buildings of the village provide a clue as to what is underneath. Abbotsbury lies on Jurassic limestone and its buildings have been constructed with this beautiful golden stone. Cotswold villages are similarly lucky as are some in north Dorset and Somerset near quarries of Ham Hill Stone. Iron is often responsible for the colour of rocks, and this is the case in this instance. The golden colour comes from oxidised iron, indicating that the sediments were perhaps deposited in relatively shallow waters where oxygen was available.

WALK 2

West Bay

P Start

East Cliff

Burton
Freshwater

Burton
Cliff

Burton Beach

Burton Bradstock

Finish
P

Hive Beach

Walk 3 - West Bay to Burton Bradstock

Distance	1.9 miles (3km)
Estimated time	1-1½ hours
Difficulty	●●○○○
Ascent	130ft (40m)
Map	OS Map OL 15
Starting point	SY 463904

Notes: A short, easy walk with one or two moderate climbs. It can, of course, be done the other way round and can be extended as far as Charmouth, bearing in mind the X53 service stops at Burton Bradstock, Chideock and Charmouth. This area of coast is particularly susceptible to rockfalls. Please take great care, follow all local safety notices and check on www.southwestcoastpath.org.uk for recent announcements. At the time of writing, the National Trust has closed the Burton Beach between Hive and Freshwater.

This walk follows two magnificent stretches of sandstone cliffs, East Cliff and Burton Cliff. The coast path at West Bay can be accessed from the beach east of the harbour entrance. From here follow the path all the way to Hive Beach. At Burton Freshwater you will need to follow the path a little way inland alongside the river and cross over the bridge. Follow the path along the other side of the river towards Burton Cliff. The cliff path is closed just before Hive Beach. Follow the diverted path to the left, turn right at the small road (Southover) and, where it joins Cliff Road, follow the path across the field to Hive Beach; or carry on along the B3157 (Common Lane) to the intersection with Beach Road and the bus stop.

WALK 3

The Bridport Sands near Burton Beach.

The dramatic cliffs at Burton Beach and east of West Bay are largely composed of Bridport Sands, although at Burton they are capped by other, younger Jurassic rocks. The sands date from the top of the Lower Jurassic and are around 175 million years old. In the early part of the Jurassic Dorset was covered by quite deep seas in which the thick sequences of blue/grey clays, typical of Lyme Bay, were deposited. By this time, however, the seas were more shallow and it is thought the Bridport Sands were laid down at the front of a huge delta, the river of which brought down material from land to the north. This is supported by the fact that the sands get older as you trace them northwards, suggesting that the delta grew southwards.

The Bridport Sands are naturally a blue/grey colour; the striking reds and oranges we see in the cliffs are the result of oxidation at the surface. Look at freshly broken pieces and you may see the original colour. It is easy to see that the strata in the Bridport Sands

The Harbour at West Bay.

are lying almost horizontally, much as they were when they were first deposited. The layers are easy to pick out because of the numerous harder bands, which stand out of the cliffs due to the fact that they are more resistant to weathering than the softer sediment in between. It seems that from time to time there was a greater concentration of calcium carbonate in the sea and as it precipitated out has acted as a cement for the sandstone, resulting in a much harder texture. Geologists have speculated that storms might have been responsible for bringing more organic

detritus into this area of deposition, particularly of animals which used calcium carbonate for hard parts. As we look at the cliffs we can appreciate the cyclical nature of these environmental changes. At West Bay it is noticeable that the harder layers are more closely spaced at the top of the cliffs than at the bottom. Does this mean that the stormy times became more frequent or that the supply of sand was decreasing? Either way it is yet another example of how variations in the rocks we see tell us about changing environments millions of years ago.

The wonderful sandstone cliffs at West Bay.

WEST BAY
(Gateway Town)

EAST CLIFF

BURTON BRADSTOCK

BURTON CLIFF

RIVER BRIT

COOMBE COURT

INFERIOR OOLITE

RIVER BRIDE

FULLERS EARTH CLAY

INFERIOR OOLITE

BLIND BARROW

FOREST MARBLE

BRIDPORT SANDS Harbour Mouth

BRIDPORT SANDS

BRIDPORT SANDS

46N

47N
02° 45' W

48N

89E C H E S I L

49N

B E A C H

Thorncombe
Beacon

Finish P

Seatown

West Bay

P

Start

Eype Mouth

Walk 4 - West Bay to Chideock

Distance	3.8 miles (6km)
Estimated time	2 hours
Difficulty	●●●··
Ascent	470ft (140m)
Map	OS Map OL 15
Starting point	SY 462904

Notes: The climb up Thorncombe Beacon is fairly steep. The energetic may want to combine this walk with Walk 6 from Chideock to Charmouth and do the whole section from West Bay to Charmouth in one go. Bus services run between The George Hotel, West Bay, and the bridge at Chideock a number of times daily. This area of coast is particularly susceptible to landslips. Please take great care, follow all local safety notices and check on www.southwestcoastpath.com for recent announcements.

Park in West Bay and follow the road around the west side of the harbour and along the sea front. The coast path begins to ascend the cliffs as the road ends. This can then be followed easily all the way to Seatown, first down to Eype Mouth before climbing up Thorncombe Beacon and down to Seatown. This part of the coast path is also part of the Monarch's Way, a long distance footpath that follows the route taken by the future King Charles II as he fled from the battlefield at Worcester in September 1651. After many adventures, including some notable narrow escapes in Dorset, he finally escaped to France. From Seatown, Sea Hill Lane leads inland to Chideock.

WALK 4

At West Bay the spectacular orange cliffs of the Bridport Sands suddenly give way to slumped cliffs of grey clay, west of the harbour entrance. In this instance this change of rock type along the coast is not the result of the tilting of the strata but a consequence of faulting. Faults such as these are the result of tension in the Earth's crust, often caused when parts of the crust are uplifted. They may also be the result of 'settling' of strata after a tectonic event. The cliffs between Seatown and Eype are composed of Lower Jurassic clays and sandstones, the youngest being the Bridport Sand. Capping that are Middle Jurassic rocks, a thin limestone, the Inferior Oolite and above that, the Fuller's Earth. Between Watton Cliff and West Bay, two large faults have thrown the rocks down, bringing the Middle Jurassic Fullers Earth level with the Lower Jurassic rocks further west. Slightly to the west of the harbour entrance a fault has resulted in the younger Bridport Sands being thrown down level with the older Jurassic rocks. Between West Bay and Seatown there are a number of such faults, which further complicates the geology and it often takes an experienced geological eye to unravel the strata at such locations. It is worth noting that where, on the coast, you see valleys or breaks

Looking west from West Bay.

in the cliffs, and perhaps different rocks on either side, this may well be caused by a fault (see section below).

Much of the grey clay in the cliffs to the west of West Bay are made of a rock called Fuller's Earth. The descriptive name of this rock stems from the fact that its absorbent properties led to its use in fulling or the degreasing of wool. The Fuller's Earth here is not suitable for this process which depends on the absorption qualities of different types of clays.

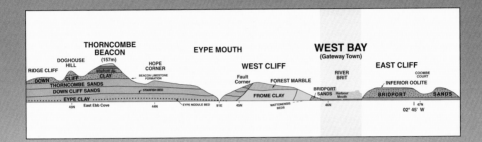

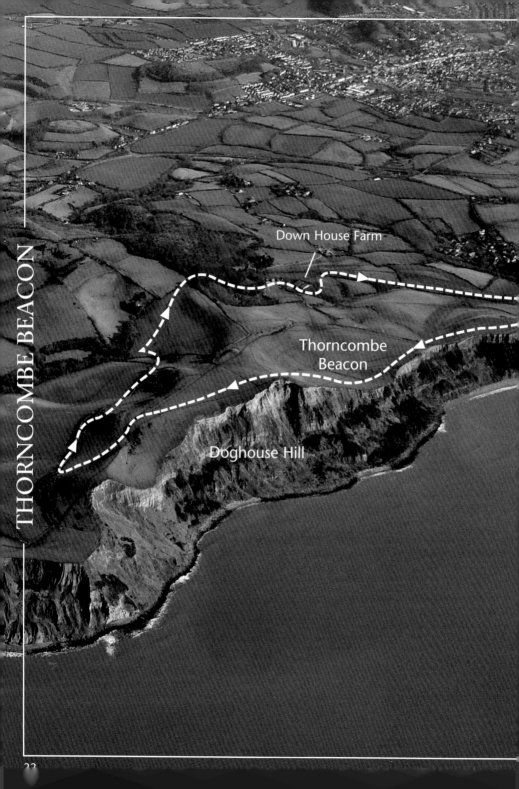

Down House Farm

Thorncombe Beacon

Doghouse Hill

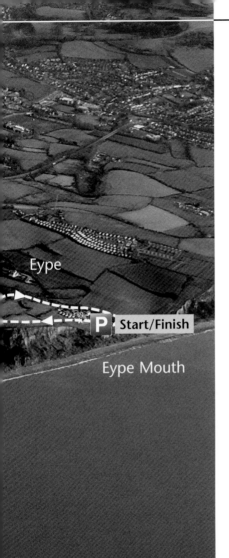

Eype

Eype Mouth

P Start/Finish

Walk 5 - Thorncombe Beacon

Distance	2.8 miles (4.5km)
Estimated time	1¾ -2 hours
Difficulty	●●●◦◦
Ascent	400ft (120m)
Map	OS Map OL 15
Starting point	SY 448911

Notes: An initial steep climb up to Thorncombe Beacon, gentle thereafter. This area of coast is particularly susceptible to landslips. Please take great care, follow all local safety notices and check on www.southwestcoastpath.org.uk for recent announcements.

From the small car park at Eype Mouth take the coast path westwards up to Thorncombe Beacon. Near Eype Mouth runs one of the most important faults in the region. It trends east-west and the southern side has been downthrown. Apart from the very top, which is Cretaceous, the bulk of Thorncombe Beacon is composed of the Jurassic Bridport Sands. Look east from the top of the Beacon and you will see the Bridport Sands of the cliffs at West Bay much lower down; they are on the downthrown side of the fault.

Carry on past Doghouse Hill and then follow the path round the back of the hill keeping to the field boundaries. Follow this until you reach a stile on the left. Go over this and then immediately right through a gate and up the hill. At the top in the corner of the field follow the footpath that leads through the woods. You will emerge at Down House Farm, an organic farm on National Trust land with

WALK 5

The wonderful view eastwards along the coast from Thorncombe Beacon.

a popular café and restaurant. From here take the path to Lower Eype.

Palaeogeography is the study of landscape in past ages. We have already seen how the process of plate tectonics has resulted in the distribution of land and sea constantly changing. Most of the rocks on which our cities, towns and villages are built were formed at the bottom of oceans, often shallow but occasionally very deep. The rocks of the Jurassic Coast provide a record of these changes over 185 million years of Earth's history. During this time Dorset and East Devon were never very far away from land and the rocks we find here come from both marine and non-marine environments; the latter including deltas, estuaries, lakes and freshwater lagoons. Such a situation also means that a wonderful variety of fossils are found on the Jurassic Coast site, including animals and plants from land and sea.

Standing on top of Thorncombe Beacon is a good place to appreciate these ancient environments. At the very top you are standing on Cretaceous sandstones, which lie unconformably on Jurassic sandstones (see Walks 7 and 11 for more on unconformities). Beneath these are the Jurassic Bridport Sands, while at the base of the cliff are Jurassic clays. The change in rock type reflects changes in ancient geography.

Superbly preserved brittle-starfish have been found between Eype and Seatown.

The path, across fields, back
towards Eype Mouth.

Sandstones are often indicative of
a formation relatively near land
since sand grains are dropped quite
quickly, while finer clay particles
drift further out to sea. Looking
westwards and inland we see the
effect these differences have had on
modern-day geography; the Jurassic

clays form the rich, fertile vales
surrounded by hills capped with the
harder sandstones and limestones.
This beautiful landscape is being
slowly eroded by rivers, which
empty their detritus back into the
sea ready to form a new generation
of sedimentary rocks.

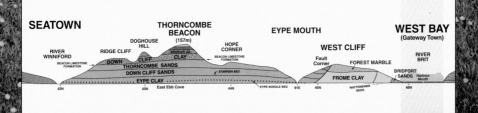

Finish

Charmouth

P

Golden Cap

Walk 6 - Chideock to Charmouth

Distance	4.4 miles (7km)
Estimated time	2½ hours
Difficulty	●●●○○
Ascent	500ft (150m)
Map	OS Map OL 15
Starting point	SY 422928

Notes: Some moderate climbs. The paths can be very muddy after wet weather. This area of coast is particularly susceptible to landslips, take note of warnings and follow any diversion signs that may be in place. Check on www.southwestcoastpath.org.uk for recent announcements. Local bus services stop at both Chideock and Charmouth.

At Chideock take the road down to Seatown until you reach Pettycrate Lane on the right. Turn into this lane, and continue up it, keeping right when the path forks then left at the next junction. Follow the signs to Golden Cap. There are steps that lead right to the top where there is a triangulation point. Then follow the coast path all the way to the beach at Charmouth. The road leads up to the centre of the village where you can find the bus stop near the church.

WALK 6

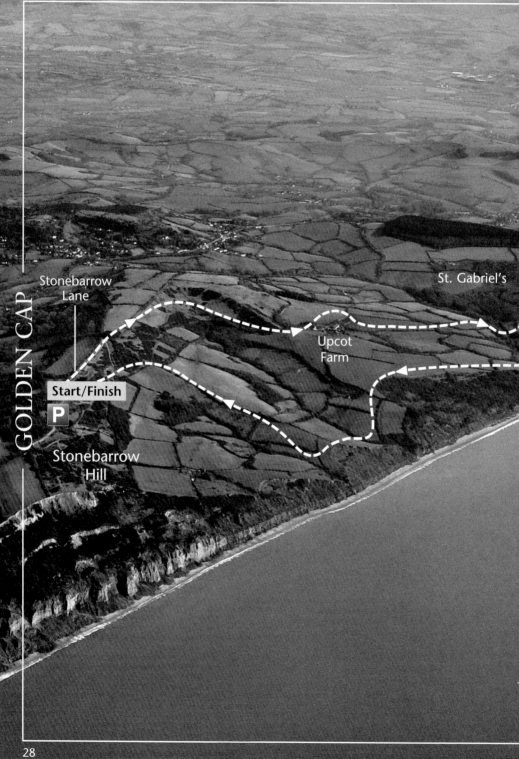

GOLDEN CAP

Stonebarrow
Lane

St. Gabriel's

Upcot
Farm

Start/Finish

P

Stonebarrow
Hill

Golden Cap

Walk 7 - Golden Cap

Distance	4 miles (6.5km)
Estimated time	2½ hours
Difficulty	●●●●
Ascent	660ft (200m)
Map	OS Map OL 15
Starting point	SY 382934

Notes: One or two steep climbs.

Start east of Charmouth at the National Trust car park at the end of Stonebarrow Lane where there is plenty of parking. Follow the gravel road or the path alongside it until you see a sign to St Gabriel's and Golden Cap. Take this path and continue to Upcot Farm. From here follow the path to the left through the farm and then almost immediately turn right to St Gabriel's. This must once have been a charming village but it is still a beautiful spot with a tranquil atmosphere. The manor has been turned into holiday cottages by the National Trust and from the ruined church there are lovely views over the coast.

Take the path past the church to Golden Cap. It leads diagonally across the field to the shoulder of the great cliff. Turn right and follow the coast path. Continue until you see a path on the right for Stonebarrow. Take this and near the top turn left on a track which takes you back to the car park.

WALK 7

The path down from Golden Cap.

GOLDEN CAP

At 619 feet above sea level, Golden Cap is said to be the highest cliff in southern England. It owes its name and height to the capping of the relatively hard Cretaceous Upper Greensand formation that sits on top of Jurassic clays. The cliff is not so golden as it used to be due to increased vegetation around the top.

Cretaceous strata lie on top of Lower Jurassic clays: you might be wondering where the rest of the Jurassic, and for that matter, the Lower Cretaceous rocks have gone. Where is the Fuller's Earth, the Kimmeridge Clay, the Portland Limestone, the Purbeck and Wealden Bed? Thousands of metres of strata are missing here at Golden Cap.

The simple answer is that they have been eroded away; Golden Cap is one of a number of places on the Jurassic Coast where the Great Unconformity

is on show (see Walk 11). Sometime during the Lower Cretaceous, earth movements caused this part of the world to be uplifted. It became land and any Upper Jurassic and Lower Cretaceous rocks that had been deposited were eroded. The sedimentary strata were also tilted by the Earth movements, so when the sea returned during the Cretaceous Period, subsequent sedimentary strata were laid down at an angle to these older rocks. Further west in Devon Cretaceous strata lie directly on top of Triassic layers, the entire Jurassic has been eroded away.

Unconformities are important geological features; they help us piece together the record of earth movements and marine transgressions caused by the relentless movements of the plates of the Earth's crust. In some places they are easier to spot than others. When continents collide and great mountain chains are thrown up, rocks can be intensely folded. Subsequent erosion can reduce the mountains to lowland areas so that when the sea returns and new sediments are laid down we may see flat strata lying unconformably on highly contorted sedimentary layers. If you look carefully, for example at the cliff sections east of Lyme Regis, you should be able to see flat Cretaceous sandstones lying on slightly tilted Jurassic rocks.

By looking at the sequence of rocks at a particular locality geologists can build up a history of that place; by considering many other places as well they can build a much wider ranging history.

Landslips on the coast path towards Charmouth.

CHARMOUTH
(Gateway Town)

STONEBARROW
(148m)

GOLDEN CAP
(191m)

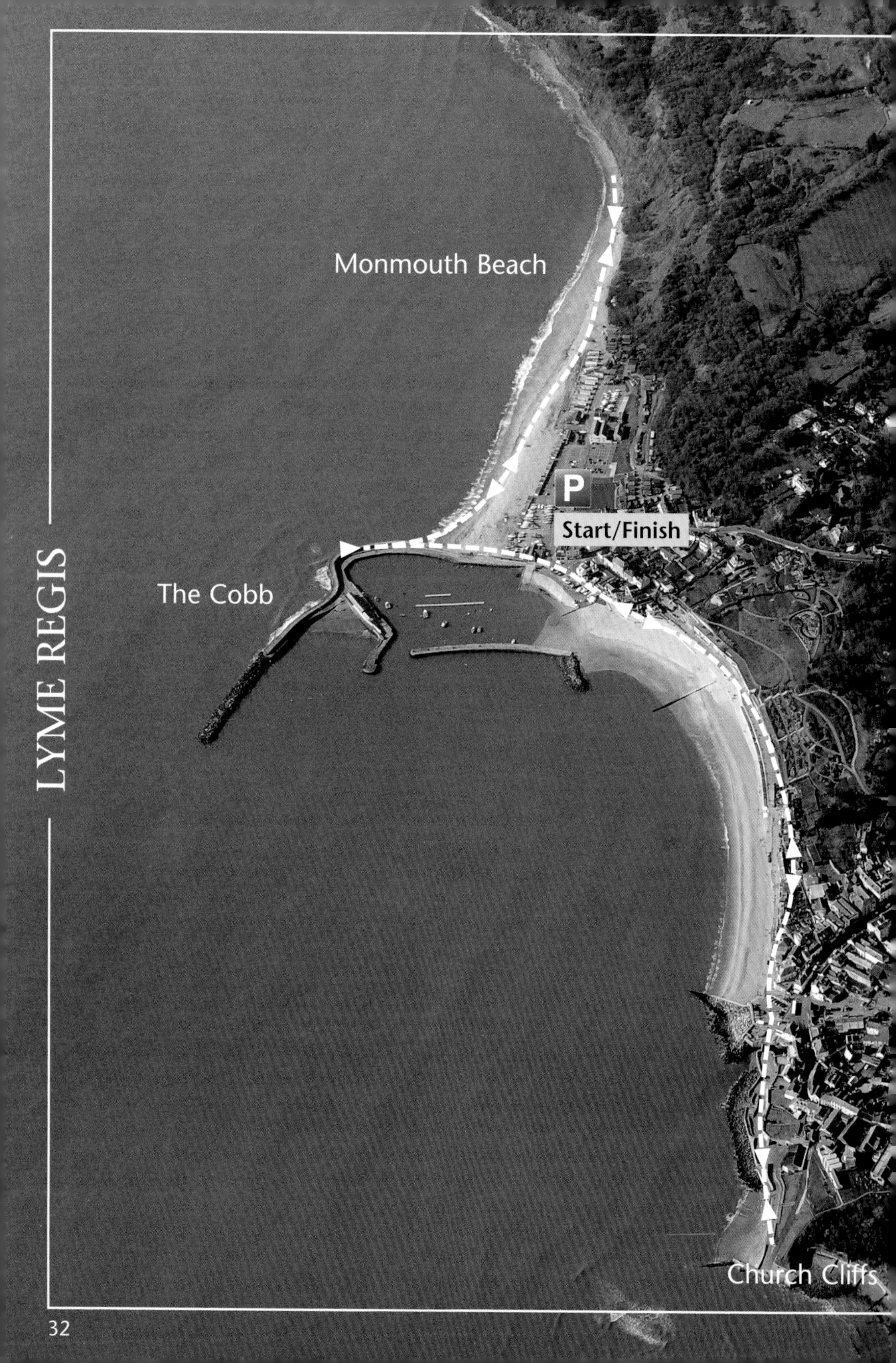

LYME REGIS

Monmouth Beach

P
Start/Finish

The Cobb

Church Cliffs

P

Lyme Regis

Walk 8 - Lyme Regis

Distance	1.25 miles (2km)
Estimated time	As long as you like!
Difficulty	●●●●●
Ascent	0ft (0m)
Map	OS Map OL 15
Starting point	SY 337915

Notes: Take note of any warnings. This area of coast is particularly susceptible to landslips so stay away from the cliffs at all times. Please take great care, and check on www.southwestcoastpath.org.uk for recent announcements.

This is simply a stroll along the seafront at Lyme Regis, from Monmouth Beach in the west to Church Cliffs in the east. This is one of the best-known and most popular fossil collecting locations in the country. It hardly needs to be said that the cliffs are very unstable and that it is not a good idea to look for fossils in them or scramble around the bottom. Please do not hammer the cliffs. Instead look around the foreshore, in pebbles and crumbled clay layers that have slipped and been worked by the waves. There are many ammonites of all sizes exposed in the "Ammonite Pavement" at the far end of Monmouth Beach; it is an amazing sight and only exposed at low tide. These cannot be taken home of course, but why not try another form of fossil collecting through photography? These ammonites make excellent photographic subjects; the surrounding pebbles adding wonderful texture. There are a number of fossil shops in the town with superb specimens, and don't forget a visit to the town museum.

WALK 8

Monmouth Beach, Lyme Regis.

The cliffs at Lyme Regis are largely made of Lower Jurassic clays with bands of limestone. These rocks were formed in the seas that followed the desert conditions of the Triassic Period. The great supercontinent of Pangaea had begun to break up and Dorset was situated in a newly formed sea on one of the breaks. Following the mass extinctions before the Triassic, life had blossomed again and the Jurassic seas were beginning to teem with life: the record of this is in the cliffs and on the beaches at Lyme Regis, with more and more evidence continually being exposed by regular landslips.

Reptiles ruled the land, sea and air. The dinosaurs had escaped the extinctions relatively unscathed and began to evolve rapidly, while the sea was dominated by giant reptiles such as the ichthyosaurs and plesiosaurs. Lyme Regis's famous fossil collector, Mary Anning, uncovered

the first full skeleton of an ichthyosaur in 1811 and thirteen years later unearthed the first plesiosaur. You will be very lucky to discover such remarkable fossils but it is difficult to walk along Monmouth Beach without noticing superb ammonites gradually being weathered out of pebbles and boulders. Ammonoids (the order containing ammonites) had been almost wiped out in the Permian extinction, but some types survived and evolved during the Triassic. The ammonites proper evolved from these forms and flourished in the tropical seas of the early Jurassic.

We have a good idea how they lived because a distant cousin, the nautilus, still inhabits the Earth's oceans. They would have moved upright through the water squirting water to propel themselves and controlling their buoyancy by regulating the gas in their chambered shells. Their soft parts were housed in the large first chamber and tentacles would

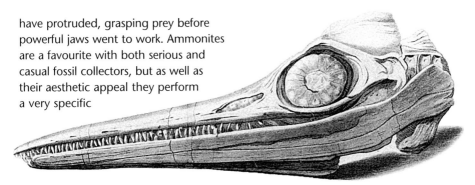

have protruded, grasping prey before powerful jaws went to work. Ammonites are a favourite with both serious and casual fossil collectors, but as well as their aesthetic appeal they perform a very specific

function for geologists. Ammonites evolved rapidly with some species dying out as others proliferated. Consequently individual species can be used to define time zones and are known as 'zone fossils'. This is particularly useful as it means that when a certain species is found in a different type of rock many miles away, that rock can be correlated as being the same age as other rocks in which the same fossil appears. This helps geologists build up a picture of what conditions prevailed at a certain time.

One of the ways in which ammonites evolved was in the complexity of the divisions between the shell chambers. It seems that as time went on they became more and more elaborate and this is evident by the suture lines just below the shell which represent the end of the divisions.

The first well-preserved ichthyosaur fossil to come to scientific attention was found by Mary Anning in 1811.

Mary Anning
Perhaps the most famous past resident of Lyme Regis was Mary Anning (1799–1847). Inspired by her father and left destitute by his death, Mary helped her mother develop their fossil collecting business. Through local knowledge, business acumen, self-taught scientific knowledge and tremendous determination she became the most famous fossil collector of her age. Today many of her finds are displayed in the Natural History Museum, including the first complete specimens of an ichthyosaur and a plesiosaur. Mary's grave is at the church of St. Michael the Archangel in Lyme Regis.

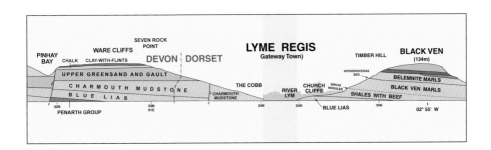

Branscombe

P

HOOKEN CLIFFS

Hooken
Cliffs

Beer Head

Beer

Start/Finish P

Walk 9 - Hooken Cliffs

Distance	3.1 miles (5km)
Estimated time	1¾ hours
Difficulty	●●○○○
Ascent	470ft (140m)
Map	OS Explorer Maps 115/116
Starting point	SY 228888

Notes: Just one fairly steep climb.

The starting point for this walk is the large car park to the south of the village of Beer towards Beer Head.

Take the coast path south towards Hooken Cliffs. At the top of the cliffs take the coast path to the left, which leads down through the landslip. The path emerges at Branscombe Mouth. If you wish, take time to explore this beautiful village. When you are ready to leave, follow the path back up to Hooken Cliffs, this time on the more direct route over the top.

When you reach a coastguard lookout tower take the path to the left, which leads back to the car park or, if you prefer, return along the same cliff top path.

WALK 9

Looking towards Seaton from Beer Head. The Chalk and the sandstone have been brought together by a fault.

HOOKEN CLIFFS

Landslips are a characteristic feature of much of the Jurassic Coast. Hooken Cliffs are perhaps a unique example in that the effect is arguably more pleasing on the eye than the original landscape. As you wander along the lower footpath that meanders through the displaced chalk it almost feels like you are exploring a lost world. Although landslips cause understandable concern over the erosion of the coastline they are partly responsible for the Jurassic Coast receiving its World Heritage status. Over the years they have revealed countless valuable fossils that have enabled scientists to unravel the story of life through this era. They continue to do so and, as the fallen material is washed by the sea, specimens are left on the shoreline to be found by dedicated collectors and eager tourists. As with all fossil collecting, you are most strongly advised to stay away from the cliffs at

View of Branscombe.

all times as rock falls are an ever present hazard. The responsible collector can always find good specimens if he or she follows the published safety advice and local announcements.

The Hooken landslip took place in March 1790. Overnight a great crack opened up behind the cliffs. It is estimated that around 7–10 acres of land then slipped about 200 feet into the sea, causing lobster pots offshore to be raised about 15 feet out of the water! Some of the great chunks of Chalk slipped almost intact, keeping

Two views of the Hooken landslip, one a drawing from 1840, and the other showing the path that runs through it today.

Stages of a landslip

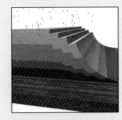

Stage 1
Lower Jurassic rocks form a benched cliff capped by the Upper Greensand.

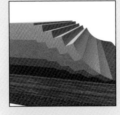

Stage 2
Rain water percolates through the sand but cannot pass through the clay.

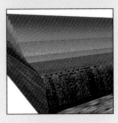

Stage 3
Water builds up at the junction between the rocks and seeps out as springs.

Stage 4
After periods of prolonged rainfall, water pressure builds up and the cliffs fail.

its orientation. The reasons behind this dramatic event are not hard to understand. First, the strata here are gently inclined, dipping out towards the sea. Secondly, the Chalk and Upper Greensand rest (unconformably) on Mercia Mudstone. As water percolates through the porous Chalk and Greensand it eventually meets the impervious mudstone, causing water pressure to build, forming a well-lubricated layer, enabling the strata above to simply slide off into the sea.

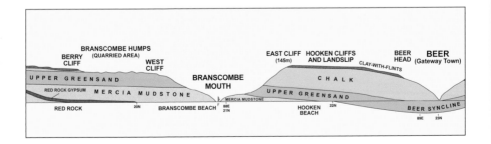

SALCOMBE HILL TO SIDMOUTH

Norman Lockyer
Observatory

Start

Sidmouth

Finish **P**

Salcombe Hill

Walk 10 - Salcombe Hill to Sidmouth

Distance	1.4 miles (2.3km)
Estimated time	1 hour
Difficulty	●●●●●
Ascent	0ft (0m)
Map	OS Explorer map 115
Starting point	SY 139883

Notes: The Sidmouth Hopper is a free hail and ride circular bus that runs in Summer between the Sidmouth Bus Triangle and the Observatory. For timetable information please check with Sidmouth Tourist Information Centre on 01395 516441 or see www.visitsidmouth.co.uk

From the Norman Lockyer Observatory follow the path leading south from the car park on the other side of the road. This leads to Salcombe Hill from where there are great views over Sidmouth and the coastline.

Sidmouth is an archetypal gentle, English seaside town. Like other small settlements along this coast, Sidmouth was originally a fishing village, its importance limited by the impossibility of making a safe harbour there. When it did expand in the Regency era, it was because of the new fashion of holidaying at the seaside. Today Sidmouth retains a 'timeless charm', words used by John Betjeman who loved the town and made a television documentary about it in 1962. With beautiful gardens and the lovely Regency buildings flanking the Esplanade, Sidmouth remains a great place to relax by the sea.

Follow the coast path down into Sidmouth; note that it is quite steep in places.

WALK 10

Sidmouth

Norman Lockyer
Observatory

Start/Finish

P

Salcombe
Hill

SALCOMBE HILL

Salcombe
Mouth

Salcombe Regis

Walk 11 - Salcombe Hill

Distance	1.9 miles (3km)
Estimated time	2 hours
Difficulty	●●●●●
Ascent	320ft (90m)
Map	OS Explorer map 115
Starting point	SY 139882

Notes: The climb up Salcombe Hill Cliff from Salcombe Mouth is steep. See Notes for Walk 10 for details of the local bus service from Sidmouth to Salcombe Hill and Observatory.

This walk starts at the National Trust car park near the Norman Lockyer Observatory on Salcombe Hill, east of Sidmouth. The observatory can be visited on a number of open days and group bookings can be made.

Follow the main track south from the car park then turn left by the house on a path across a field. At the end of the field turn left towards a wood. When you reach the wood follow the path on the right that leads down through the wood. At the end of this turn right and follow the tarmac road past a farm. Continue on the path as it follows the contours of the hill. When you reach the cliff turn right down a valley, across a stream and up the coast path on the other side. Go over the brow of the hill towards Sidmouth and you will see a track on the right which leads back to the car park.

Looking eastwards towards Salcombe Hill from the beach at Sidmouth.

Either side of Salcombe Mouth stand high cliffs capped by the Upper Greensand formation. Beneath the Greensand is the soft Mercia Mudstone, a combination that has led to the characteristic rolling hills of this part of Devon. The stream that reaches the sea at Salcombe Mouth has eroded the mudstones relatively easily and it is consequently a steep, tiring climb to the cliff top on either side.

What we can see is known as the 'Great Unconformity'(see also Walk 7); the Mercia Mudstone is Triassic and the Greensand is Cretaceous; the entire Jurassic is missing. Although the great thickness of mudstone may seem a rather uninteresting rock, it has a fascinating story to tell us about these ancient environments.

The Otter Sandstone, on which it lies, was formed by rivers flowing northwards across desert regions. The Mercia Mudstone represents much quieter conditions, probably a playa lake in an arid or semi-arid basin surrounded by mountains. Such lakes often dry out and, as such, are usually associated with salt deposits.

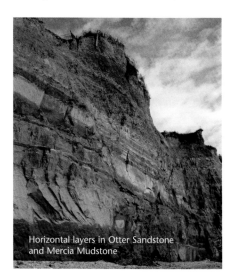

Horizontal layers in Otter Sandstone and Mercia Mudstone

Salcombe Mouth; the start of the long climb up Salcombe Hill.

The presence of veins of gypsum in the mudstone is one of the indicators to the environment of deposition. Although conspicuous fossils are few and far between, evidence of land plants has confirmed a continental origin. Playa lakes are found in many places today and by comparing the sediments that are collecting in modern examples, geologists can infer conditions that existed millions of years ago. The assumption behind this reasoning is one of the great principles of geology 'uniformitarianism',

Norman Lockyer Observatory

Salcombe Hill is the home of the Norman Lockyer Observatory. This historic optical observatory is now owned by East Devon District Council and was founded in 1912 by Sir Norman Lockyer. It is run by the Norman Lockyer Observatory Society and aims to promote the natural sciences, particularly astronomy. There are a number of open evenings during the year when, for a small charge, you can look around, attend presentations and, if the sky is clear, look through the telescopes. Additionally the Society runs tutorials where you can go into aspects of astronomy in more detail. Full details are available on their website, www.normanlockyer.com

proposed by the Victorian pioneer, Sir Charles Lyell. Sometimes summarised as 'the present is the key to the past', it assumes that the same processes were at work at the Earth's surface millions of years ago as exist today.

WALK 11

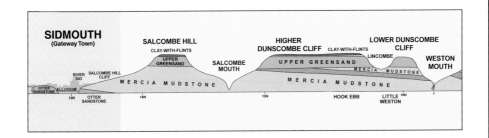

Sidmouth

Start P

Dunscombe
Cliff

Salcombe
Mouth

Weston
Cliff

Finish **P**

Branscombe

Walk 12 - Sidmouth to Branscombe

Distance	5.6 miles (9km)
Estimated time	3-4 hours
Difficulty	●●●●●
Ascent	1200ft (350m)
Map	OS Explorer map 115
Starting point	SY 129874

Notes: The climbs are steep and can be slippery in wet weather. This area of coast is particularly susceptible to landslips. Please take great care and ensure you have plenty of water. Follow all local safety notices and check on www.southwestcoastpath.org.uk for recent announcements. The Coasthopper 899 bus service runs Monday to Saturday between Branscombe Village Hall and Sidmouth Triangle. See www.travelinesw.com

At the eastern end of the promenade at Sidmouth a small footbridge crosses the River Sid. From here the coast path leads steeply up the cliff and it is simply a case of following it all the way to Branscombe. In the first half of the walk there are two steep climbs, first from Salcombe Mouth up Dunscombe Cliff, and secondly from Weston Mouth up Weston Cliff. Needless to say these are preceded by steep descents. However, from Weston Cliff the path is reasonably level until it descends again to Branscombe Mouth.

If you plan to do the walk in the opposite direction it is worth noting that the steep climbs will come during the second half of the walk!

Otterton

LADRAM BAY

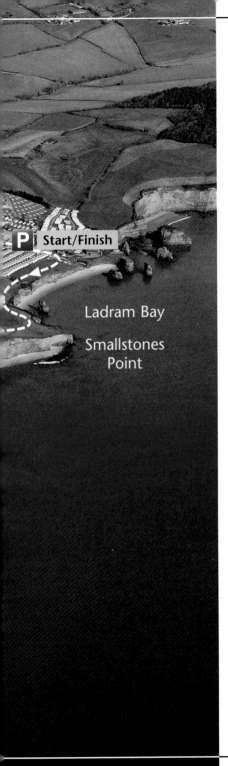

Ladram Bay

Smallstones Point

Start/Finish

Walk 13 - Ladram Bay

Distance	1.9 miles (3km)
Estimated time	1¼ hours
Difficulty	●○○○○
Ascent	170ft (50m)
Map	OS Explorer 115
Starting point	SX 096854

Notes: A very easy walk.

From Ladram Bay Holiday Park follow the coast path south around Smallstones Point. There are excellent views of the bay from this path. Carry on along this path, ignoring the first path to the right to Otterton, take the next right on a 'permissive path'. This will lead you to Stantyway Road. Follow this quiet, beautiful road to Otterton. Turn right and follow the road back to Ladram Bay and the holiday park.

On the east side of the Otter Estuary the Otter Sandstone is again exposed. This was deposited by rivers in an otherwise arid environment. The rivers meant that vegetation could thrive and therefore animals too. Although finds are relatively rare, the sandstone is a very important source of Triassic fossils, in particular the giant amphibians known as Rhynchosaurs. The exposure can only be reached from the coast path on the other side of the estuary (see walk 14) and shows good examples of 'rhizoconcretions' which are the fossilised remains of plant roots and can be easily identified.

WALK 13

Otter Sandstone at Ladram Bay.

The red Otter Sandstones at Ladram Bay were formed in the Triassic Period around 230 million years ago. At that time Dorset and Devon were situated at about latitude 10° North. It was hot and arid and, perhaps intuitively, we recognise these rocks as coming from a desert environment. However, although we may class a desert environment as arid, this does not

Cross-bedding in the sandstones at Ladram Bay.

mean there is no water. Rivers do flow through many desert regions, fed by distant mountains; and many are also subject to flash flooding. Consequently not all desert sediments consist of wind blown sands.

The cliffs at Ladram Bay provide us with an easily recognisable clue to their origin. Cross-bedding – thin, curved layers that cut across each other – is a sign of either wind or river deposition. In deserts, layers of sand build up in dunes, which then migrate and change direction with the wind. This creates the crisscross pattern we see in the rocks. Changing river channels can produce the same effect and this is what we see at Ladram Bay. There are a number of ways of distinguishing wind-deposited sandstones from those laid down in rivers, but generally the cross-bedding in desert dunes is on a much larger scale than that produced by river channels.

Ladram Bay is well known for its sea stacks, – isolated columns of sandstone that are products of erosion. The way in which rocks erode is controlled to some extent by the pattern of joints within the rocks. Joints are planes of weakness and at Ladram Bay erosion along the near vertical joints has led to the broadly rectangular stacks. The stacks at Ladram Bay are somewhat protected by a harder rock around the base.

One of the sea stacks at Ladram Bay.

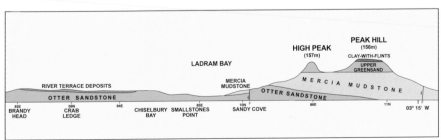

OTTERTON LEDGE

Otterton

Start/Finish

P

Colliver Cross

Otter Estuary
Nature Reserve

Ladram Bay

Otterton
Ledge

Walk 14 - Otterton Ledge

Distance	4.4 miles (7km)
Estimated time	1¾-2 hours
Difficulty	●●●●●
Ascent	120ft (35m)
Map	OS Explorer map 115
Starting point	SX 087841

Notes: An easy walk with no steep climbs. It is possible to start and finish the walk in Budleigh Salterton. From the large car park at the eastern end of the beach follow the coast path up the western side of the river and cross it at the first bridge. Now follow the route described from the entrance to the farm shop, returning over the bridge.

At the end of the tarmac on Stantyway Road leading from Otterton it is usually possible to park on the grass at the side of the road. Take the path marked 'permissive path to coast' heading east. Follow this to the coast path where there are excellent views over Ladram Bay. Head south along the coast path to Otterton Ledge and then follow it around the headland and up the side of the Otter Estuary. After you pass the entrance to a farm shop take the small tarmac road uphill to the right – do not follow the road across the river. Continue up this road and as soon as you have passed some stone gate pillars take the bridleway on the right to Colliver Cross. At the end of this bridleway turn right up the tarmac track and follow it round to Stantyway Road, keeping to the public footpath signs.

Ladram Bay

OTTER ESTUARY

Walk 15 - Otter Estuary

Distance	2.8 miles (4.5km)
Estimated time	1 hour
Difficulty	●○○○○
Ascent	30ft (10m)
Map	OS Explorer map 115
Starting point	SX 073820

Notes: A flat, easy walk.

There is a large car park next to the Otter Estuary Nature Reserve, a 57-acre Site of Special Scientific Interest. It comprises saltmarsh and mudflats and is home to a large and varied population of wintering wildfowl and waders.

Follow the path at the northwestern end of the car park that leads northwards behind a row of houses. A small stream/canal is on the right. Follow the path until it sweeps round by an aqueduct to follow the river southwards. Continue back to the car park.

Today the Otter Estuary is blocked by a spit of pebbles that forces the river to meander around its tip. This unusual feature was reputedly created by the Great Storm in 1824; it is more likely that it was considerably enlarged. Some think that this storm was responsible for washing up many of the larger pebbles on the beach. Pebbles from Budleigh Salterton are found on many beaches along the south coast as far as Hastings, and it has long been thought that such storms are a major factor in transporting sediment along coastlines.

West Down Beacon

Golf Course

BUDLEIGH SALTERTON

Start/Finish

Knowle

Budleigh
Salterton

P

Walk 16 - Budleigh Salterton

Distance	3.8miles (6km)
Estimated time	1¾-2 hours
Difficulty	●●●○○
Ascent	400ft (120m)
Map	OS Explorer map 115
Starting point	SY 073819

Notes: The walk begins with a long climb, but it is fairly gentle. Take care across the golf course. At the highest point there are splendid views over Exmouth and the Exe Estuary.

Budleigh Salterton derives the last part of its name from the fact that monks here made salt pans to produce salt commercially. This practice may have gone back as far as Roman times. From the seafront walk westwards up the coast path. If you haven't already done so take a few minutes to look at the start of the cliffs from the beach. The junction between the famous Budleigh Salterton Pebble Beds and the overlying Otter Sandstone is very easy to see. The bottom of the Otter Sandstone is marked by a distinctive bright yellow band; plus it has no pebbles.

The path climbs steadily but not too steeply to the East Devon Golf Course. At the highest point near West Down Beacon (there is a triangulation point at the side of the path) turn right on a path to Knowle. When you reach a path to Exmouth on your left, turn right on a path across the golf course which soon becomes a small track. Go through a kissing gate at the end and across a field. You will come to a junction of paths; turn right on a path marked 'Littleham Church path'. Carry on down the side of a

WALK 16

The beach at Budleigh Salterton looking west.

field, through a gate with the golf course on your right. Follow the path down through a wooded area to a road. Turn right and follow this road (Exmouth Road) through the town centre to the marine parade where the walk started.

In the cliffs to the west of the beach at Budleigh Salterton lie the famous Budleigh Salterton Pebble Beds. They are easily picked out: the cliff consists of two layers, the Pebble Beds at the bottom, overlain by the Otter Sandstone which displays a distinctive honeycomb weathering. As the name suggests the Pebble Beds is a formation packed with large, rounded pebbles bonded by sand.

The Pebble Beds were deposited by large, fast-flowing rivers from mountains to the south. We can tell this partly because, when the formation is traced

northwards, the pebbles get smaller. Rivers tend to drop larger material first, carrying smaller particles further downstream. Fossils have been found inside some pebbles; but these do not help us determine the age of the Pebble

The top of the Budleigh Salterton Pebble Beds.

Beds, nor indeed of the mountains from which they came. Rather they tell us the age of the sediments from which the mountains were formed.

From an examination of the rocks it seems the rivers stopped flowing relatively suddenly; the clay and sands overlying the Pebble Beds indicate a return to desert conditions. Why this happened remains a mystery. The top of the Pebble Beds is marked by a bright yellow layer. Look carefully beneath this and you might see pebbles with a more angular appearance. These pebbles have been sandblasted in a dry, windy desert environment and so mark the time when the rivers dried up.

Budleigh pebbles

The beach is made up from pebbles derived from the Budleigh Salterton Pebble Beds. The pebbles are largely quartzite. As the name suggests, this is a rock made from the mineral quartz, itself a compound of the two most common elements in the Earth's crust – oxygen and silicon. Quartzite is a metamorphic rock, formed by the application of heat and pressure to a sandstone so that the original sand grains, perhaps loosely cemented together, now fuse to form a much harder rock. This generally happens during an episode of mountain building, and the pebbles at Budleigh Salterton are thought to derive from mountains to the south, perhaps in what is now Brittany. Of course,

the sandstone that had been compressed into quartzite consisted of sand grains that had previously been eroded and then deposited by rivers or in the sea. These sand grains possibly came from volcanic rocks, perhaps from an older mountain range.

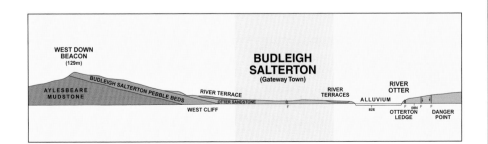

EXMOUTH

Gore Lane

Orcombe Point

P Start/Finish

Littleham Cove

Devon Cliffs Holiday Park

Walk 17- Exmouth

Distance	3.8 miles (6km)
Estimated time	2 hours
Difficulty	••◦◦◦
Ascent	230ft (70m)
Map	OS Explorer map 115
Starting point	SY 017798

Notes: Depending on the tide it is possible to walk along the beach to Sandy Bay and then climb up to the holiday park to join the coast path. Alternatively you may wish to walk along the coast path and return via the beach. Please consult the tide timetables carefully if you plan to do this.

The walk starts on the sea front near Orcombe Point just south of Exmouth. There is ample parking there. Climb the steps up to the coast path – you can either do this from the esplanade or via steps at the edge of the beach if the tide is out sufficiently. At the top of Orcombe Point is the geoneedle, the official start of the Jurassic Coast. Proceed eastwards along the coast path. When you reach the large holiday park follow the coast path signs around the site. You will not be able to follow the edge of the coast around the headland as it is a firing range.

As you pass buildings marked 'Royal Marines firing range' the path turns sharply right. Follow it across a grassy dog-walking area and start to climb the hill with Littleham Cove on your right. You will be able to see Budleigh Salterton along the coast to the east. Very soon you will see a footpath sign on the left by a hedge. Follow this through the caravan park. When you

A small fault in the red sandstones near Orcombe Point.

come to tarmac roads carry straight on (yellow sign). Proceed up through the holiday park to the main entrance. Just after the gates turn left down a narrow tarmac road. This is Gore Lane and is little used. There are lovely views over the Devon countryside. Follow it for approximately 1 kilometre until you see a path across the fields on your left signed 'Permissive path to coast'. Take this and rejoin the coast path back to the sea front by Orcombe Point.

The south coast of Devon is famous for its red sandstone cliffs, rocks that were formed in a variety of desert environments at a time when Devon and Dorset were far south of the Equator and lay roughly in the middle of the supercontinent that geologists have named Pangaea. All the world's land was joined in this one continent, a chance configuration of the wandering crustal plates.

Geological time is divided into different units. The common names that are more generally known, such as 'Triassic' and 'Jurassic', are 'periods', while several periods may be grouped as an 'era'. These divisions are based on the assemblage of fossils that the rocks contain, the life history of the planet. Clearly the periods reflect major changes in the Earth's natural history, a reminder that evolution does not progress entirely smoothly. The division into eras reflects even more major changes and at Orcombe Point at the start of the Jurassic Coast we find ourselves near

Aylesbeare Sandstone near Orcombe.

the beginning of the Triassic Period and, perhaps more importantly, of the Mesozoic Era.

Flying along the coast of East Devon one would be forgiven for thinking that the red rocks of the cliffs were all very similar. Why then do we make such a distinction between the Triassic rocks that start around Orcombe Point (the actual boundary is disputed). and the Permian rocks to the west that look so similar yet are classified as being from an earlier era? The answer lies in what happened to life on Earth at this time. At the end of the Permian Period about 250 million years ago around 90 per cent of all marine species were wiped out and about 70 per cent of the species on land. Cataclysmic events, such as a meteorite impact or large-scale volcanic eruptions, may have had something to do with this, but consider for a moment what the red rocks along this coastline tell us. If the continents became joined as a supercontinent, the Earth's climate would have been drastically altered. The interior of this supercontinent would likely be a vast, arid desert and the coastline much shortened, meaning fewer habitats on the continental shelves. This must have had a huge impact on many species. If you had looked at the Earth from above, probably you would have seen a largely

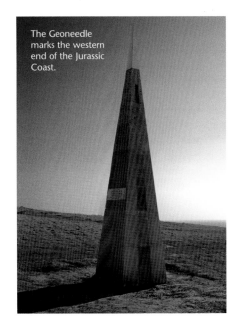

The Geoneedle marks the western end of the Jurassic Coast.

red landmass with a green fringe.

East Devon was roughly in the middle of Pangaea and the rocks are from a variety of desert environments. Some were formed in 'playa' lakes, temporary features which periodically dry out leaving flat salt pans. Others were deposited by rivers flowing from mountains to the south and west, while some were wind blown sediments, revealing the characteristic structures of desert dunes.

WALK 17

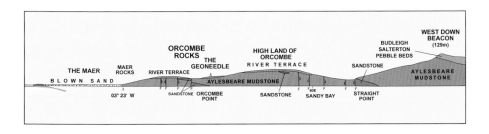

SAFETY
On the beach and coast path

- Stay away from the base of the cliffs and the cliff top and ensure that children and dogs are kept under control.
- Do not climb the cliffs. Rockfalls can happen at any time.
- Beware of mudslides, especially during or after wet weather.
- Always aim to be on the beaches on a falling tide and beware of the incoming tide, especially around headlands. Be sure to check the tide tables.
- Beware of large waves in rough weather, especially on steeply shelving beaches.
- Observe all permanent and temporary warning signs; they advise on hazards and dangers. Check routes beforehand by visiting www.southwestcoastpath.org.uk
- Be very careful on rocky foreshores which often have slippery boulders.
- Stay within your fitness level – some stretches of coast can be strenuous and/or remote.
- Make sure you have the right equipment for the conditions, such as good boots, waterproof clothing and sun screen if appropriate.
- Follow The Countryside Code.

Emergencies

In an emergency dial 999 or 112 and ask for the Coastguard, but be aware that mobile phone coverage in some areas is very limited.

FOSSILS
Collecting fossils

- The best, and safest place to look for fossils is on the beach, away from the base of the cliffs, where the sea has washed away soft clay and mud.
- Do not collect from or hammer into the cliffs, fossil features or rocky ledges.
- Keep collecting to a minimum. Avoid removing in situ fossils, rocks or minerals.
- The collection of specimens should be restricted to those places where there are plenty of fossils.
- Only collect what you need... leave something for others.
- Never collect from walls or buildings. Take care not to undermine fences, bridges or other structures.
- Be considerate and don't leave a site in an unsightly or dangerous condition.
- Do not use a hammer on flint or chert, which shatter into sharp fragments.
- Some landowners do not wish people to collect – please observe notices.

The West Dorset Fossil Collecting Code of Conduct

- This applies between Lyme Regis and Burton Bradstock.
- Collectors are asked NOT to dig in the cliffs without permission.
- Important fossil finds should be registered at the Charmouth Heritage Coast Centre.
- The full code is available from Charmouth Heritage Coast Centre or by logging onto www.charmouth.org/chcc

---

The Jurassic Coast Trust is the organisation that proudly has the responsibility for looking after England's only natural World Heritage Site, the Jurassic Coast. The Trust is a small charity with a huge remit and big ambitions for the Dorset and East Devon Coast, and we would love you to get involved. Go to **jurassiccoast.org/inspired** for more details.

The South West Coast Path covers 630 miles from Minehead to Poole, this National Trail leads you through diverse landscapes, all with their own unique story to tell. To find out more about the longest and most popular of the UK's 15 national trails, and the South West Coast Path Association, visit **www.southwestcoastpath.org.uk**